These poems belong to

....

From

....

Published by:
Candlestick Press, Diversity House, 72 Nottingham Road,
Arnold, Nottingham NG5 6LF

www.candlestickpress.co.uk

Design and typesetting by Diversity Creative Marketing Solutions
Ltd., www.divewrsity.agency

Printed by Ratcliff & Roper Print Group, Nottinghamshire, UK

Illustrations © Ruth Green, 2014, www.ruthgreendesign.com
and © Craig Twigg, 2017

Second edition, revised 2017

ISBN 978 1 907598 52 4

Acknowledgements:
Our thanks to Spike Milligan Productions Ltd for permission to
reproduce 'The Squirdle' by Spike Milligan from *A Children's
Treasury of Spike Milligan* (Virgin Books, 1999). 'My Name is'
by Pauline Clarke is from *Silver Bells and Cockle Shells* (Abelard
Schuman Ltd, 1962) and is reproduced by permission of Curtis
Brown Group Ltd, on behalf of Pauline Clarke, © 1962, Pauline
Clarke. 'The Nonny', © James Reeves, 1960, is reprinted from
Complete Poems for Children (Faber Finds) by permission of the
James Reeves Estate. 'Where Does the Bounce Come From?' by
Michael Rosen from *Centrally-Heated Knickers* (Puffin, 2000) is
printed by permission of United Agents www.unitedagents.co.uk on
behalf of Michael Rosen.

Every effort has been made to trace and contact copyright holders
of material included in this pamphlet. The publisher apologises
if any material has been included without permission or without
the appropriate acknowledgement, and would be glad to be told
of anyone who has not been consulted.

Where poets are no longer living, their dates are given.

The Nonny

The Nonny-bird I love particularly;

    All day she chirps her joysome odes.

She rises perpendicularly,

    And if she goes too far, explodes.

James Reeves (1909 – 1978)

Where Does the Bounce Come From?

Rubber dubber

flouncer bouncer

up the wall

and in and outer

under over

bouncing backer

mustn't dropper

mustn't stopper

in-betweener

do a clapper

in-betweener

do a spinner

faster faster

to and fro-er

rubber dubber

flouncer bouncer

BUT

then oh bother!

Butter finger

dropped the ball

and pitter patter

patter pitter

rubber ball

ran right away.

Michael Rosen

The Squirdle

I thought I saw a Squirdle

I think I thought I saw

I think I thunk I thought

I saw a Squirdle by my door

If it was not a Squirdle

I thought I thunk I saw

Then what in heaven's name was it

That gave a Squirdle roar?

Perhaps I saw a Pussel-skwonk!

But that would be absurd

Because I think I thunk it was

A Squirdle that I heard

So if I saw a Pussel-skwonk

Yet heard a Squirdle roar

It means I think I thunk I thought

I'd seen what I had saw!

Spike Milligan (1918 – 2002)

Untitled

The horny-goloch is an awesome beast,

Soople an scaly;

It has twa horns, an a hantle o feet,

An a forkie tailie.

Anon

My Name Is...

My name is Sluggery-wuggery

My name is Worms-for-tea

My name is Swallow-the-table-leg

My name is Drink-the-sea.

My name is I-eat-saucepans

My name is I-like-snails

My name is Grand-piano-George

My name is I-ride-whales.

My name is Jump-the-chimney

My name is Bite-my-knee

My name is Jiggery-pokery

And Riddle-me-ree, and ME.

Pauline Clarke (1921 – 2013)

Thea, perhaps you could write one for Fox?

Now it's your turn to write a nonsense poem or draw a picture of a horny-goloch!